JOB

A MASQUE FOR DANCING

Founded on

BLAKE'S

ILLUSTRATIONS OF THE BOOK OF JOB

By GEOFFREY KEYNES *and*
GWENDOLEN RAVERAT

Music by

R. VAUGHAN WILLIAMS

Full Score

OXFORD UNIVERSITY PRESS
MUSIC DEPARTMENT
44 CONDUIT STREET, LONDON W.1

ORCHESTRATION

Three Flutes (Piccolo) (Bass Flute)
Two Oboes
Cor Anglais
Two Clarinets (and 3rd Clarinet *ad lib.*, doubled by Bass Clarinet)
Bass Clarinet
E♭ Saxophone. (May be doubled by Bass Clarinet player, the Bass Clarinet
      notes being cued to the 2nd Clarinet. When the Saxophone is
      doubled by the Bass Clarinet player, the part should be omitted
      till Scene VI.)

Two Bassoons
Double Bassoon
Four Horns
Three Trumpets
Three Trombones
Tuba
Two Harps
Organ
Timpani
Percussion (Side Drum, Triangle, Bass Drum, Cymbals, Xylophone,
      Glockenspiel, Tam-Tam)

Strings

The following are *ad lib.*:—
3rd Flute (2nd Flute must then double Piccolo)
2nd Oboe
3rd Clarinet
Bass Clarinet
Saxophone
Double Bassoon
3rd Trumpet
2nd Harp
Organ
Most of the percussion.
All these are cued in.

NOTE

The music of *Job* was first performed in concert form at the Norwich
Festival, 1930. The first stage performance was given by the Camargo
Society at the Cambridge Theatre, London, 1931. Choreography by
Ninette de Valois. Scenery and dresses designed by Gwendolen Raverat.
Musical Director, Constant Lambert.

The music is scored for full symphony orchestra, but a version for small
theatre orchestra has been made by Constant Lambert.

Orchestral material is available on hire from the Publishers.

The purchase of this score or the hire of orchestral material do not convey the
right to perform, permission for which must be obtained from the Oxford
University Press or its agents.

SYNOPSIS

The following synopsis and the more detailed scenario printed with the music differs in some particulars from the original scheme of the authors. For these alterations the composer alone is responsible.

SCENE I

'Hast thou considered my servant Job?'

Introduction. Pastoral Dance. Satan's appeal to God. Saraband of the Sons of God.

Job and his family sitting in quiet contentment surrounded by flocks and herds. Satan enters unperceived and appeals to heaven. God answers: 'All that he hath is in thy power.'

SCENE II

'So Satan went forth from the presence of the Lord.'

Satan's Dance.

God's throne is empty. Satan in wild triumph seats himself upon it.

SCENE III

'Then came a great wind and smote the four corners of the house and it fell upon the young men and they are dead.'

Minuet of the sons and daughters of Job.

Job's children are feasting and dancing: Satan appears and destroys them.

SCENE IV

'In thoughts from the visions of the night . . . fear came upon me and trembling.'

Job's dream. Dance of plague, pestilence, famine and battle.

Job is quietly asleep. Satan leans over him and evokes terrible visions which dance round him, foreboding his tribulation to come.

SCENE V

(No break between Scenes IV and V)

'There came a Messenger.'

Dance of the Messengers.

The messengers announce to Job the destruction of all his wealth and the death of his sons and daughters. Job still blesses God.

SCENE VI

'Behold, happy is the man whom God correcteth.'

Dance of Job's comforters. Job's curse. A vision of Satan.

Satan introduces Job's comforters, three wily hypocrites. Their dance is at first one of apparent sympathy, but gradually changes to rebuke and anger. Job curses God. 'Let the day perish wherein I was born.' Job invokes his vision of God. Heaven opens and reveals Satan seated on God's throne. Job and his friends cower in terror.

SCENE VII

(No break between Scenes VI and VII)

'Ye are old and I am very young.'

Elihu's dance of youth and beauty.

'Then the Lord answered Job.'

Pavane of the Heavenly Host.

Enter Elihu, who is young and beautiful. Heaven opens again and shows God sitting on His throne surrounded by the heavenly host.

SCENE VIII

'All the Sons of God shouted for joy.'

Galliard of the Sons of the Morning.

'My servant Job shall pray for you.'

Altar dance and heavenly pavane.

Satan appeals again to God but is driven down by the Sons of the Morning. Job and his household build an altar and worship God with musical instruments. The heavenly dance continues.

SCENE IX

(No break between Scenes VIII and IX)

'So the Lord blessed the latter end of Job more than his beginning.'

EPILOGUE

Job, an old and humbled man, sits again surrounded by his family. He blesses his children.

To Adrian Boult

JOB

SCENE I

INTRODUCTION

R. VAUGHAN WILLIAMS

Largo sostenuto ♩ = 48*

FLUTES I & II

FLUTE III
(also Bass Fl. & Picc.)

OBOES I & II

COR ANGLAIS

CLARINETS I & II
in B♭

SAXOPHONE in E♭
(Tacet till letter F?)

BASS CLARINET
in B♭
later ch. to Clar. III in B♭
(ad lib.)

FAGOTTI I & II

CONTRAFFAGOTTO

I & II
HORNS in F
III & IV

I & II
TRUMPETS in B♭
III

I & II
TROMBONES
III & TUBA

TIMPANI

PERCUSSION
(Tri. S.D. Cym. B.D.
Xyl. Glock. Tam tam.)
(3 players required)

I
HARPS
II

ORGAN (ad lib.)
Tacet till Scene VI

VIOLINI I

VIOLINI II

I
VIOLE
II

I
VIOLONCELLI
II

CONTRABASSI

II SOLO
pp molto sost.

Bass Fl. in G
p sost. molto

pp sost.

Mutes on

Mutes on

I Mute on

G B♭ D

I SOLO
p molto sost.

p sost.

p sost.

p sost.

p sost.

p sost.

Div.**
pp molto sost.

Largo sostenuto ♩ = 48*

*The metronome marks are approximate   **Divide in proportion of 1 player on upper part to 3 on the lower part

© Copyright, 1934, by the Oxford University Press, London

Printed in Great Britain

OXFORD UNIVERSITY PRESS, MUSIC DEPARTMENT, 44 CONDUIT STREET, LONDON, W. 1

Curtain rises. Scene (back cloth) as in Blake Illustration I.
Job with his wife and a few servants sitting. Shepherds
and husbandmen cross the stage, and salute him

OXFORD UNIVERSITY PRESS MUSIC DEPARTMENT, 44 CONDUIT STREET, LONDON, W.I.

Here the distant landscape lights up
suggesting the far off sound of flocks and herds.

Here Job's children enter and group themselves round him.

5

Dance of Job's sons and daughters. First the women dance alone.

Allegro piacevole (♩.=♪)

Allegro piacevole (♩.=♪)

B Here the men dance.

6

Here the women group themselves in the middle and the men move slowly round them. Then vice versa.

L'istesso tempo (♩ = ♩.)

Here the dance becomes general.

L'istesso tempo (♩ = ♩.)

Job stands up and blesses his children, saying 'It may be my children have sinned' The dance continues.

Fl. I
Fl. II & III
Ob. I & II
C. A.
Cl. I & II in B♭
B. Cl. in B♭
Fag. I & II
C. Fag.
I & II
Hns. in F
III & IV
I & II
Trpt. in B♭
III
Trb. I & II
Trb. III & Tuba
Timp.
Harp I
Harp II
Vln. I
Vln. II
Vle
Celli
C.B.
cresc.
p cresc.
pp II SOLO
III Trb.
Tuba
a 2
Fl. II
take Bass Fl.
ff sost.
ff
f
f sost.
III mute on
legato
f ma non troppo
tr

Everyone kneels. Tableau as in Blake I. Angels appear at the side of the stage as in Blake II and V.

The group breaks up into two on each side of the stage. All go off except Job and his wife who are left in meditation down stage (the Angels however remain)

II

Heaven gradually opens and displays God sitting in majesty, surrounded by the sons of God (as in Blake II)
The line of Angels stretches from Earth to Heaven.

Andante con moto ♩=80

Andante con moto ♩=80

SARABAND OF THE SONS OF GOD

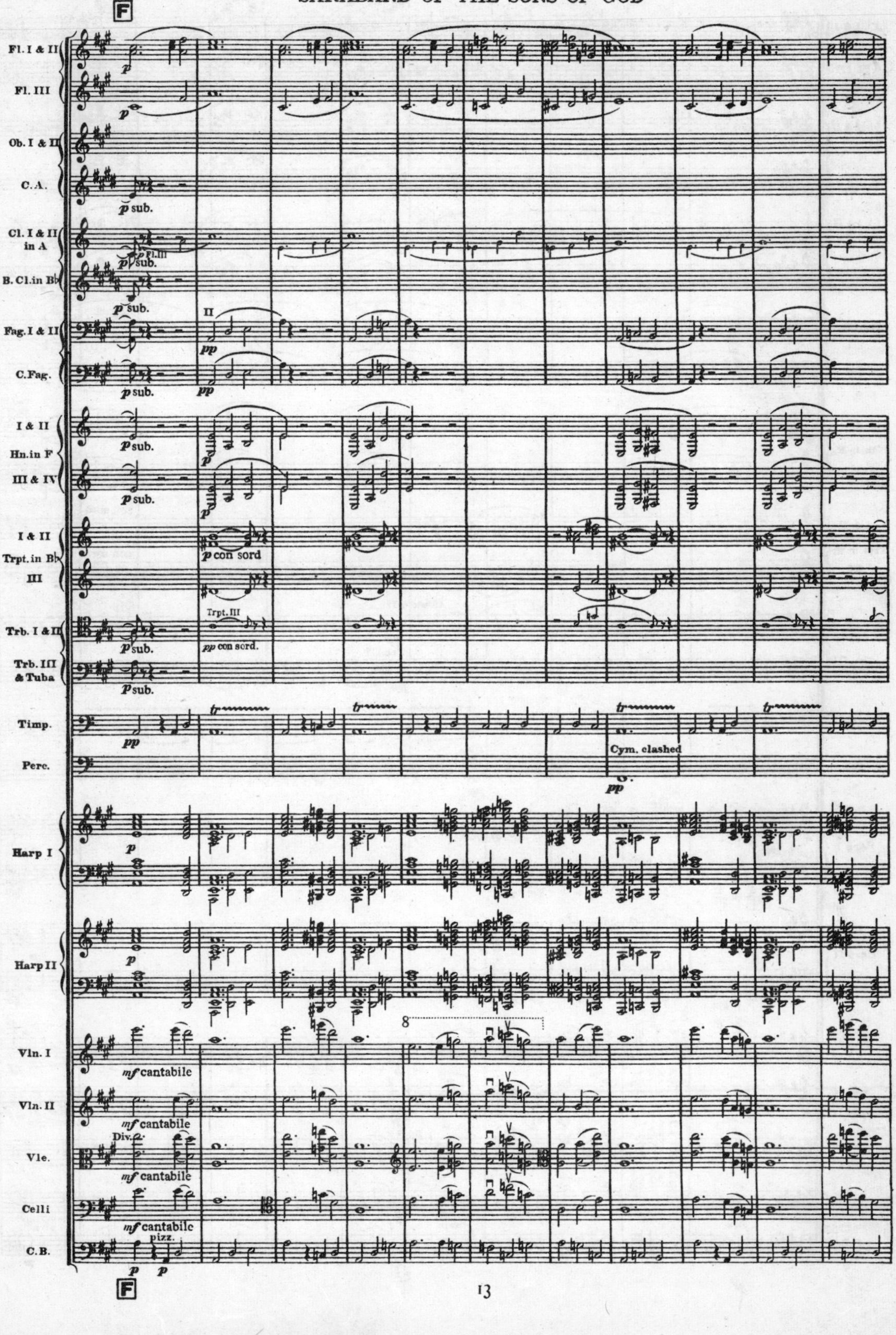

All bow down in adoration

God arises in His majesty
and beckons to Satan.

Satan steps forward at God's command.

15

A light falls on Job. God regards him with affection and says to Satan 'Hast thou considered my servant Job'.

Satan says 'Put forth Thy hand now and touch all that he hath and he will curse Thee to Thy face'.

16

God says 'All that he hath is in thy power.' Satan departs (see Blake V)
K Largamente
a2
ff
Fl. I & II
Picc.
Ob. I & II
C. A.
Cl. I & II in A
B.Cl. in B♭
Fag. I & II
C. Fag.
I & II
Hn. in F
III & IV
I & II
Trpt. in B♭
III
Trb. I & II
Trb. III & Tuba
Harp I
Harp II
Mutes off
senza sord.
Vln. I
Vln. II
Vle.
Celli
C. B.
pizz
C.Fag. (arco)
K Largamente

The dance of homage begins again. God leaves his throne

M The stage darkens.
Black out.
Fl. I & II
Picc.
Ob. I & II
C.A.
Cl. I & II in A
B.Cl. in B♭
Fag. I & II
C Fag.
I & II
Hn. in F
III & IV
I & II
Trpt. in B♭
III
Trb. I & II
Trb. III & Tuba
Timp.
Perc.
B.D. roll
Cymbals splashed
Harp I
Harp II
Vln. I
Vln. II
Vla.
Celli
C.B.
Ob. II
mutes on
III mute
M

SCENE II
SATAN'S DANCE OF TRIUMPH

Stage gradually lightens.. Heaven is empty and God's throne vacant. Satan alone on the stage.

Presto (1 in the bar) ($\downarrow$. = 96)

Presto (1 in the bar) ($\downarrow$. = 96)

20

A light falls on Satan, standing
at the bottom of the steps of
Heaven (Tableau till letter P)

21

Fl. I & II
Picc.
Ob. I & II
C. A.
Cl. I & II in A
B. Cl. in B♭
Fag. I & II
C. Fag.
I & II
Hn. in F
III & IV
I & II
Trpt. in B♭
III
Trb. I & II
Trb. III & Tuba
senza sord.
Trom. III
Timp.
Perc.
Xylo
Vln. I
Vln. II
Vle.
Celli
C. B.
p
dim.
ff
pp
mf

P *Here the dance begins*

If the dance is too long for one performer, other dancers may be introduced; *or*, all the repeats may be omitted.

Fl. I & II
Picc.
Ob. I & II
C. A.
Cl. I & II in A
B. Cl. in B♭
Fag. I & II
C. Fag.
I & II
Hn. in F
III & IV
I & II
Trpt. in B♭
III
Trb. I & II
Xylo.
Vln. I
Vln. II
Vle.
Celli
C. B.
a 2
dim.
pp

Q
Fl. I & II
Picc.
Ob. I & II
C. A.
Cl. I & II in A
B. Cl. in B♭
Fag. I & II
C. Fag.
I & II
Hn. in F
III & IV
Trpt. I, II & III
Trb. I & II
Trb. III & Tuba
Tuba
Xylo.
Vln. I
Vln. II
Vle.
Celli.
C.B.
a 2
pp cresc.
p cresc.
cresc.
dim.
arco
non div.
p
mf
ff
f
Q

Fl. I & II
Picc.
Ob. I & II
C. A.
Cl. I & II in A
B. Cl. in B♭
Fag. I & II
C. Fag.
I & II
Hn. in F
III & IV
I & II
Trpt. in B♭
III
Trb. III & Tuba
Timp.
Perc.
Vln. I
Vln II
Vle
Celli
C.B.
a2
ff
Wooden sticks
Cymbals clashed

27

28

Fl. I & II
Picc.
Ob. I & II
C. A.
Cl. I & II in A
B. Cl. in B♭
Fag. I & II
C. Fag.
I & II
Hn. in F
III & IV
I & II
Trpt. in B♭
III
Trb. III & Tuba
S.D.
Cymbal roll
Perc.
Vln. I
Vln. II
Vle
Celli
C.B.
p
pp
cresc.

Moderato alla marcia (♩=♩.)

T
Fl. I & II
Picc.
Ob I & II
C.A.
Cl. I & II in A
B.Cl. in B♭
Fag. I & II
C. Fag.
I & II
Hn. in F
III & IV
I & II
Trpt. in B♭
III
Trb. I & II
Trb. III & Tuba
Timp.
Perc.
Harp I
Harp II
Vln. I
Vln. II
Vle.
Celli
C.B.
a2
f pesante
ff
Cym. clashed
p
T

a 2
Fl. I & II
Picc.
a 2
Ob. I & II
C.A.
Cl. I & II in A
B.Cl. in B♭
Fag. I & II
C. Fag.
I & II
Hn. in F
III & IV
I & II
Trpt. in B♭
III
Trb. I & II
Trb. III & Tuba
Timp.
Perc.
Cym.
Xylo.
Harp I
Harp II
Vln. I
Vln. II
Vle.
Celli
C.B.

Presto
Fl. I & II
Picc.
Ob. I & II
C.A.
Cl. I & II in A
B.Cl. in B♭
Fag. I & II
C. Fag.
I & II
Hn. in F
III & IV
I & II
Trpt. in B♭
III
Trb. I & II
Trb. III & Tuba
Timp.
Perc.
Xylo.
Harp I
Harp II
Vln. I
Vln. II
Vle.
Celli
C. B.
a2
Mutes on
con sord.
a2 (Pedal notes)
D in C
div.
unis.
pizz.
Presto

Satan climbs up
to God's throne

34

Fl. I & II
Picc.
Ob. I & II
C. A.
Cl. I & II in A
B. Cl. in B♭
Fag. I & II
C. Fag.
I & II
Hn. in F
III & IV
con sord.
I & II
Trpt. in B♭
III
Trb. I & II
Tuba
Trb. III & Tuba
Timp.
S.D.
Perc.
Xyl.
Vln. I
Vln. II
Vle.
Celli
C. B.

V
Satan kneels in mock adoration before God's throne
Fl. I & II
Picc
Ob. I & II
C. A.
Cl. I & II in A
B. Cl. in B♭
Fag. I & II
C. Fag.
I & II
Hn. in F
III & IV
I & II
Trpt. in B♭
III
Trb. I & II
Trb. III & Tuba
Timp.
Perc.
Xyl.
Vln. I
Vln. II
Vle.
Celli
C. B.
a 2
p cresc.
senza sord.
Tuba
8va ad lib.
con sord.
Trom. III
'Glor - - - i-a in ex - cel - sis De - o.'
Cym. struck
V

Fl. I & II
Picc.
Ob. I & II
C.A.
Cl. I & II in A
a 2
B. Cl. in B♭
Fag. I & II
C. Fag.
I & II
Hn. in F
III & IV
I & II
Trpt. in B♭
III
Trb. I & II
Trb. III & Tuba
Tuba 8va bassa
Timp.
Perc.
dim.
B.D.
Cyms. struck
Xyl.
Vln. I
Vln. II
Vle.
Celli
C. B.

The hosts of Hell enter running, and kneel before Satan, who has risen and stands before God's throne facing the audience.

Satan with a big gesture sits in God's throne

Black-out; a black curtain falls leaving the front quarter of the stage visible.

39

SCENE III
MINUET OF THE SONS OF JOB AND THEIR WIVES

Enter Job's sons and their wives and dance in front of the curtain. They hold golden wine cups in their left hands which they clash at + (each time). The Dance should be formal, statuesque and slightly voluptuous, it should not be a minuet as far as choreography is concerned.

Here the black curtain draws back and shows an interior as in Blake III

*Solo cello play when no Bass Clar. otherwise play col tutti

I SOLO
Fl. I & II
Fl. III
Fl. III take Picc.
Ob. I & II
C.A.
B.Cl. in B♭
Fag. I & II
Hn. I & II in F
Timp.
Perc.
Harp. I
Vln. I
Vln. II
Vle.
Bass Clar.
Cello Solo
Celli Tutti
(Solo col Tutti)
C.B.
Fl. I
Fl. II
Picc.
C.A.
Bass Clar.
Cl. I & II in A
B.Cl. in B♭
Fag. I & II
Perc.
Tri.
Vln. I
Vln. II
Vle
Solo Vle. cue for Bass Clar.
div.
Celli
C.B.

Fl.I & II
Picc.
C.A.
Cl.I & II in A
B.Cl.in B♭
Fag.I & II
Hn.I & II in F
Perc.
Vln.I
Vln.II
Vle.
Celli
C.B.
Bass Clar.
a2
II Mute on
div.
arco
Z
I & II Hn. in F III & IV
Trpt.I & II in B♭
Timp.
Harp I
con sord.
sostenuto
B.D.
Cyms.
pizz.

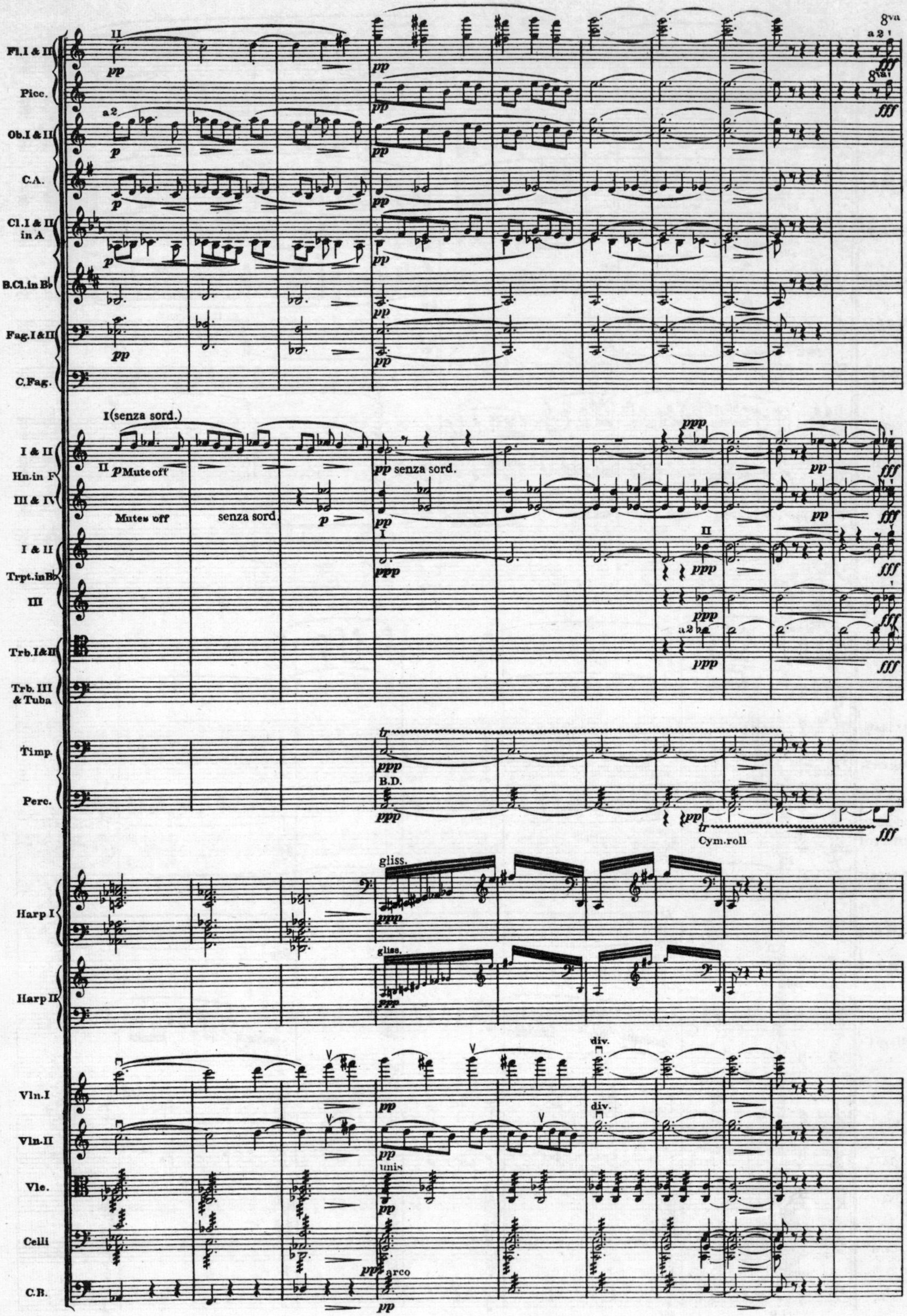

Enter Satan above. The dance stops suddenly.
The dancers fall dead. Tableau as in Blake III.

Aa

Aa

Fl. I & II
Picc.
Picc. take Fl.
Fl. III
Ob. I & II
(Oboe II)
C.A.
Cl. I & II in A
B. Cl. in B♭
Fag. I & II
C. Fag.
I & II
Hn. in F
III & IV
Trpt. III in B♭
Trb. I & II
Trb. III & Tuba
Trb. III
Timp.
Perc.
Cyms.
Vln. I
Vln. II
Vle.
Celli
C.B.
dim.
a 2

Gradual black out. The black curtain descends.

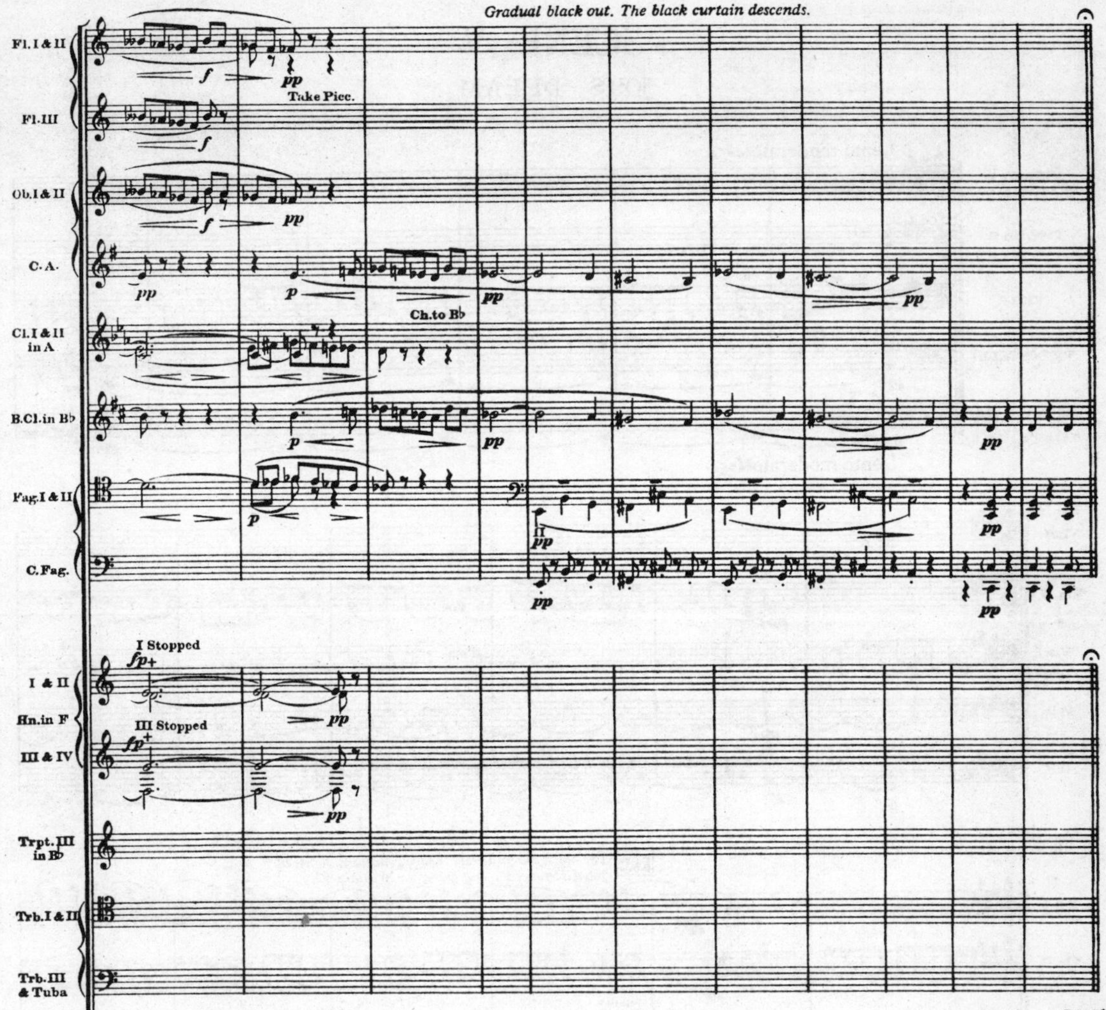

SCENE IV
JOB'S DREAM

* In the Blake illustrations, Scene V (Messengers) follows here. Producers who wish to follow Blake's order exactly can do so by making a pause (⌒) at the double bar here and going straight on to Scene V.

Job moves uneasily in his sleep.

Allegro (♩=180)

Enter Satan. Tableau as in Blake VI. Satan stands over Job and calls up ter-
rifying Visions of Plague, Pestilence, Famine, Battle, Murder and SuddenDeath
who posture before Job (see Blake XI). Each of these should be represented by a
group of dancers. The dance should be wild and full of movement, and the
stage should finally be full.

Enter Plague and Pestilence

Enter Famine

Fl. I & II
Picc.
Ob. I & II
C.A.
Cl. in B♭
B. Cl. in B♭
Fag. I & II
C Fag.
I & II
Hn. in F
III & IV
I & II
Trpt. in B♭
III
Trb. I & II
Trb. III & Tuba
Timp.
Perc.
Vln. I
Vln. II
Vle.
Celli
C.B.
a 2
a 2
stopped
open
Trpt. III con sord.
III SOLO con sord.
S.D.
pizz.
arco

Ee
Enter Battle etc.
Fl. I & II
Picc.
Ob. I & II
C.A.
Cl. in B♭
B.Cl. in B♭
Fag. I & II
C Fag.
I & II
Hn. in F
III & IV
I & II
Trpt. in B♭
III
Trb. I & II
Trb. III & Tuba
Timp.
Perc.
Xylo.
Harp I
Harp II
Vln. I
Vln. II
Vle.
Celli
C.B.
Soli a 2
senza sord.
con sord.
naturale
S.D.
sec
pizz.
Ee

Fl. I & II
Picc.
Ob. I & II
C.A.
Cl. in B♭
B. Cl. in B♭
Fag. I & II
C Fag.
I & II
Hn. in F
III & IV
I & II
Trpt. in B♭
III
Trb. I & II
Trb. III & Tuba
Timp.
Perc.
Xylo.
Harp I
Harp II
Vln. I
Vln. II
Vle.
Celli
C.B.
Soli a2
senza sord.
a2
Cymbals clashed
sec
arco
sempre pizz.

Fl. I & II
Picc.
Ob. I & II
C. A
Clar. in B♭
B. Cl. in B♭
Fag.
C. Fag.
I & II
Hn. in F
III & IV
I & II
Trpt. in B♭
III
Trb. I & II
Trb. III & Tuba
Timp.
Perc.
Xyl.
Harp I
Harp II
Vln. I
Vln. II
Vle
Celli
C. B.
a2
Trpt. III
Tuba
p cresc.
Trom. III
pizz.
arco
non div.

The dancers headed by Satan make a ring round Job and raise their hands three times

57

Ff
Fl. I & II
Picc.
Ob. I & II
C.A.
Clar. in B♭
Sax. in E♭
B.Cl. in B♭
Fag.
C.Fag.
I & II
Hn. in F
III & IV
I & II
Trpt. in B♭
III
Trb. I & II
Trb. III & Tuba
Timp.
Perc.
Harp I
Harp II
Vln. I
Vln. II
Vle.
Celli
C.B.
a 2
SOLO
poco f
G♯ in G♮
S.D.
Cymbals clashed
Tri.
sul G

Fl. I & II
Picc.
Ob. I & II
C.A.
Clar. in B♭
Sax. in E♭
B.Cl. in B♭
Fag.
C.Fag.
I & II
Hn. in F
III & IV
I & II
Trpt. in B♭
III
Trb. I & II
Trb. III & Tuba
Timp.
Perc.
Harp I
Harp II
Vln. I
Vln. II
Vle.
Celli
C.B.

Gg
The vision gradually disappears
Fl. I & II
Picc.
Ob. I & II
Clar. in B♭
Sax. in E♭
B. Cl. in B♭
Fag.
C. Fag.
I & II
Hn. in F
III & IV
I & II
Trpt. in B♭
III
Trb. I & II
Trb. III & Tuba
Timp.
Perc.
Vln. I
Vln. II
Vle.
Celli
C. B.
ff
dim.
p
pp
mf
f
sost.
Wooden sticks
B D. roll
Cymbals clashed
Gg

* When Scene V is taken before the dance in Scene IV, make a pause (⌢) at this double bar, and go straight to Scene VI (Comforters dance).

SCENE V
DANCE OF THE THREE MESSENGERS

Job awakes from his sleep and perceives three messengers, who arrive one after the other, telling him that all his wealth is destroyed. (See Blake IV)

A sad procession passes across the back of the stage, culminating in the funeral cortège of Job's sons and their wives.

Hh Andante con moto (♩=64)

Hh *pp* Andante con moto (♩=64)

* If required by the Stage a cut may be made from **Hb** to **Kk**

Fl. I & II
Fl. III
Clar. I & II in B♭
Fag.
I SOLO
Fl. III
I & II
Hn. in F
III & IV
pp I
pp II
pp III
pp IV
Timp.
Vln. I
pp cantabile
Vln. II
Vle.
Celli.
pp cantabile
Mutes on
con sord.
C.B.
pp pizz. sempre
Kk
Fl. I & II
Fl. III
Take Piccolo
Ob.
I SOLO
mp cantabile
C.A.
Clar. I & II in B♭
Fl. III
B. Cl. in B♭
Fag.
I
mp cantabile
I & II
Hn. in F
III & IV
pp Trpt. III
(play when Horn II plays Trpt. III part)
I & II
Trpt. in B♭
III
con sord.
con sord.
pp molto legato
pp molto legato
I & II Mutes off
Timp.
Vln. I
ppp
Vln. II
con sord.
Vle.
ppp
Celli.
ppp
C.B.
arco
pp
Kk

Lento
Ob.
C.A.
Clar. I & II in B♭
B.Cl. in B♭
Fag.
I SOLO
I & II
Hn. in F
III & IV
III
I & II
Trpt. in B♭
III
Timp.
Vln. I
Vln. II
Vle.
Celli
C.B.
cantabile
Lento
Cadenza senza misura quasi lontano
(♩= 54)
Ob.
Clar. in B♭
Vln. I
Vln. II
Vle.
Celli
C.B.
(♩= 54)

Job still blesses God. 'The Lord gave and the Lord hath taken away, blessed be the name of the Lord.'

*A cut of 4 bars may be made here if required by the stage.

††When Scene V is taken before the Dance in Scene IV, turn back here to Allegro (10 bars before Cc) and play on to end of the Allegro

SCENE VI
DANCE OF JOB'S COMFORTERS

Satan introduces in turn, Job's 3 Comforters (three wily hypocrites). Their dance is at first one of pretended sympathy. But develops into anger and reproach (see Blake VII and X).

* The Saxophone part may be played by the Bass Clarinet player, the Bass Clarinet part is cued into the 2nd Clarinet

Fl. I & II
Cl. I & II in B♭
Sax. in E♭
B. Cl. in B♭
Fag.
Vln. I
Vln. II
Vle.
Celli
C. B.
Mm
Poco più mosso
Picc.
Ob.
C. A.
I & II
Hn. in F
III & IV
I & II
Trpt. in B♭
III
Trb. I & II
Trb. III & Tuba
a 2
con sord.
Trpt. III
arco
pizz.

Ancora più mosso
Fl. I & II
Picc.
Ob.
C.A.
Clar. I & II in B♭
Sax. in E♭
B. Cl. in B♭
Fag.
C. Fag.
2nd time only
I & II
Hn. in F
III & IV
2nd time only
senza sord.
a 2
I & II
Trpt. in B♭
III
Mute off
Trb. I & II
Trb. III & Tuba
(2nd time only)
Perc.
S.D.
Vln. I
Vln. II
Vle.
Celli
C. B.
Ancora più mosso

Fl. I & II
Picc.
Ob. I & II
C.A.
Cl. I & II in B♭
B. Cl. in B♭
Fag. I & II
C. Fag.
I & II Hn. in F III & IV
I & II Trpt. in B♭ III
Trb. I & II
Trb. III & Tuba
Perc.
Vln. I
Vln. II
Vle
Celli
C.B.
a 2
f
p
ff
arco
non div.
sempre pizz.

Oo
Fl. I & II
Picc.
Ob. I & II
C. A.
Cl. I & II in B♭
B. Cl. in B♭
Fag. I & II
C. Fag.
I & II Hn. in F III & IV
I & II Trpt. in B♭ III
Trb. I & II
Trb. III & Tuba
Perc.
Vln. I
Vln. II
Vle
Celli
C. B.
a 2
cresc.
ff
f
senza sord.
III
Oo

Here the comforters return to their
gestures of pretended sympathy

rit.

72

Tempo I
I Solo when no Sax.
Fl. I & II
p
molto espr.
I Solo when no Sax.
Cl. I & II in B♭
p
Sax. in E♭
p
molto espr.
Vln. I
Vln. II
pizz.
Vle
pp
Cello Solo
p
molto espr.
pizz.
div.
unis.
Celli Tutti
pp
pizz.
I Desk
C.B.
pp
Tempo I
Fl. I & II
Cl. I & II in B♭
Sax. in E♭
Vln. I
Vln. II
Vle
Cello Solo
div.
Celli Tutti
C.B.

Job stands and curses God, 'Let the day perish wherein I was born.' (see Blake VIII)

Heaven gradually becomes visible, showing mysterious veiled sinister figures,
moving in a sort of parody of the Sons of God in Scene I.

* If required by the Stage, a cut of 9 bars (to ∅) may be made here.

Fl. I & II
Fl. III
Ob. I & II
C. A.
Cl. I & II in B♭
B. Cl. in B♭
Fag. I & II
C. Fag.
I & II
Hn. in F
III & IV
I & II
Trpt. in B♭
III
Trb. I & II
Trb. III & Tuba
Timp.
Perc.
Organ ad lib.
Vln. I
Vln. II
Vle.
Celli
C. B.
a 2
ad lib.
Take Picc.
dim.
Trb. III

Heaven is now lit up. The figures throw off their veils and display themselves as Satan enthroned, surrounded by the hosts of Hell

NOTE:—Where there is an Organ with very powerful reeds the bars marked ✛ may be played by Organ and Timpani only

77

Fl. I & II
Picc.
Ob. I & II
C.A.
Cl. I & II in B♭
B. Cl. in B♭
Fag. I & II
C. Fag.
I & II
Hn. in F
III & IV
I & II
Trpt. in B♭
III
Trb. I & II
Trb. III & Tuba
Timp.
Perc.
B.D. roll
Organ ad lib.
(senza dim.)
Vln. I
Vln. II
Vle.
Celli
C.B.
div.
p cresc.
a2

Satan stands. Job and his friends cower in terror

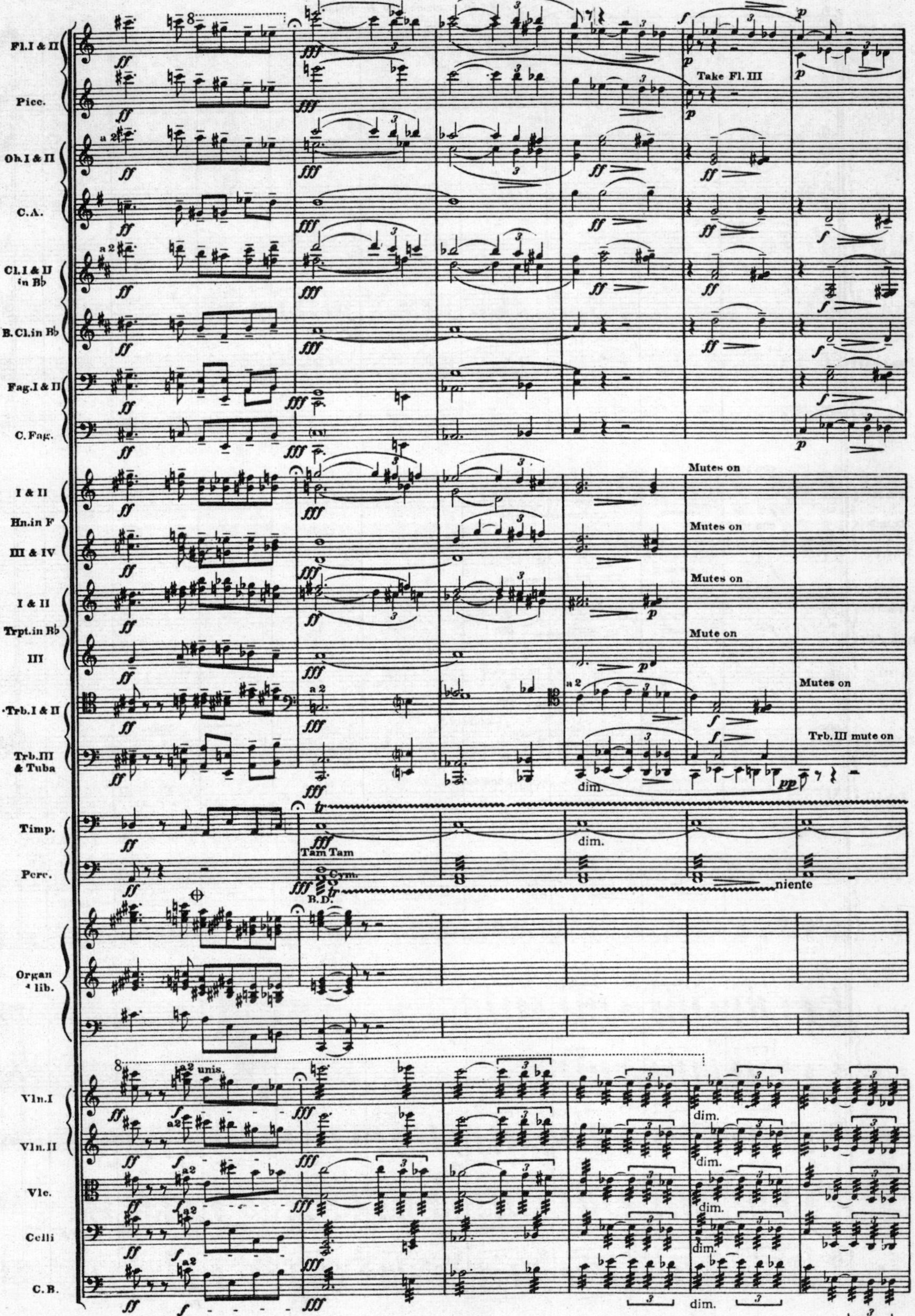

The vision gradually disappears
Fl. I & II
Fl. III
Ob. I & II
C.A.
Cl. I & II in B♭
B. Cl. in B♭
Fag. I & II
C. Fag.
Hn. in F I & II
III & IV
Trpt. in B♭ I & II
III
Trb. I & II
Trb. III & Tuba
Timp.
Perc.
Vln. I
Vln. II
Vle.
Celli
C. B.
Clars. change to A
Bass Clar.
con sord.
a 2
Mutes off
Trb. III
Mutes on
niente
A in G
C in A♭
D♭ in C
p
pp
ppp
pppp
f

SCENE VII
ELIHU'S DANCE OF YOUTH AND BEAUTY

Enter Elihu, a beautiful young man. 'I am young and ye are very old' (see Blake XII).

*If required by the Stage, a cut of 17 bars (to ♂) may be made here

Vln. Solo
Vln. I
Vln. II
Vle.
Celli.
C. B.
Poco allarg. a tempo
Harp. I
ppp
pp
pizz.
I Desk
Allegretto (𝅗𝅥 = 112)
SOLO p
Cl. in A.
Fag. I
Fag. II
Harp I
Mutes off
Poco allarg.
a tempo

Cl. in A
Fag. I
Fag. II
Harp I
Vln. Solo
Vln. I
Vln. II
Vle.
Celli.
C. B.
p cantabile
senza sord.
pizz.
pp
TUTTI
Rit. _ in tempo I
Ss
Poco allarg.
a tempo
arco div.
(pizz.)
ppp
I Desk
arco
Desk I

PAVANE OF THE SONS OF THE MORNING

Heaven gradually shines behind the stars. Dim figures are seen dancing a solemn dance. As Heaven grows lighter, they are seen to be the Sons of the morning dancing before God's Throne (see Blake XIV).

Tt
a2
Fl. I & II
Fl. III
Ob. I & II
C. A.
Cl. in A
B. Cl. in B♭
Fag. I & II
C. Fag.
I & II
Hn. in F
III & IV
I & II
Trpt. in B♭
III
Trb. I & II
Trb. III & Tuba
Timp.
tr
Perc.
Cymbals
Harp I
Harp II
Vln. I
Vln. II
I & II
Vle.
III
I & II
Celli
III
C. B.
pizz.
arco
pp
ppp
Tt

Fl. I & II
Fl. III
Ob. I & II
C. A.
Cl. in A
B. Cl. in B♭
Fag. I & II
C. Fag.
I & II
Hn. in F
III & IV
I & II
Trpt. in B♭
III
Trb. I & II
Trb. III & Tuba
Timp.
Perc.
Harp I
Harp II
Vln. I
Vln. II
I & II
Vle.
III
I & II
Celli
III
C. B.
pp
ppp
con sord.
Mutes off
A♭ to A♮, C to B♭
tr
SOLO
unis.
pizz.
arco

Fl. I & II
Fl. III
Ob. I & II
C. A.
Cl. in A
B. Cl. in B♭
Fag. I & II
C. Fag.
I & II
Hn. in F
III & IV
I & II
Trpt. in B♭
III
Trb. I & II
Trb. III & Tuba
Timp.
Perc.
Harp I
Harp II
Vln. I
Vln. II
I & II
Vle.
III
I & II
Celli
III
C. B.
a2
cresc.
Fl. III take Picc.
senza sord.
pp
ppp
p
mf
f
B.D.
Cym.
II & III

Ww
Fl. I & II
Picc.
Ob
C.A.
Cl. in A
B.Cl in B♭
Fag I & II
C.Fag.
I & II
Hns. in F
III & IV
I & II
Trpt. in B♭
III
Trb. I & II
Trb. III & Tuba
Timp.
Perc.
Harp I
Harp II
Vln. I
Vln. II
I & II
Vle.
III
I
Celli
II & III
C.B.
a2
Picc.
gliss.
unis.
arco
Cls. change to B♭
Ww

SCENE VIII
GALLIARD OF THE SONS OF THE MORNING

Enter Satan. He claims the victory over Job.

Andante con moto ($\quarter = 80$)

God pronounces sentence of banishment on Satan.

The Sons of the Morning gradually drive Satan down. (see Blake V and XVI)

Xx Largamente.

Allegro pesante (♩=160)

Xx Largamente

Allegro pesante (♩=160)

90

Yy
Fl. I & II
Fl. III
Ob.
C.A.
Cl. in B♭
B.Cl. in B♭
Fag.
C. Fag.
I & II
Hns. in F
III & IV
I & II
Trpt. in B♭
III
Trpt. III
Trb. I & II
Trb. III & Tuba
Timp.
Perc.
Harp I
Harp II
Vln. I
Vln. II
Vle.
Celli
C.B.
a 2
a 2
II
IV
f marcato
f marcato
sul G
sul G
Yy

Fl. I & II
Fl. III
Ob.
C. A.
Cl. in B♭
B. Cl. in B♭
Fag.
C. Fag.
I & II
Hns. in F
III & IV
I & II
Trpt. in B♭
III
Trb. I & II
Trb. III & Tuba
Timp.
Perc.
Harp I
Harp II
Vln. I
Vln. II
Vle.
Celli
C. B.
a2
f marcato
sim.
mf
sul G
unis.
f marc.
div.

Zz
Fl. I & II
Ob. II
Fl. III
Take Picc.
Ob.
C. A.
Cl. in B♭
a 2
B. Cl. in B♭
Fag.
C. Fag.
I & II
Hns. in F
III & IV
a 2
I & II
Trpt. in B♭
III
Trb. I & II
Trb. III
Trb. III & Tuba
Tuba
Timp.
Perc.
Tri.
Harp I
Harp II
Vln. I
unis.
sul G
Vln. II
sul G
Vle.
pizz.
unis.
arco
Celli
pizz.
unis.
arco
C. B.
pizz.
arco
Zz

AAa
Fl. I & II
Picc.
Ob.
C.A.
Cl. in B♭
B.Cl. in B♭
Fag.
C.Fag.
I & II
Hns. in F
III & IV
I & II
Trpt. in B♭
III
Trb. I & II
Trb. III & Tuba
Trb. III
Tuba
Timp.
Perc.
Tri.
Vln. I
Vln. II
Vle.
Celli
C.B.
Ob. II
a 2
marc.
div.
unis.
arco
pizz.
sul G
f
p
AAa

BBb
Fl. I & II
Picc.
Ob.
C. A.
Cl. in B♭
B. Cl. in B♭
Fag.
C. Fag.
I & II
Hns. in F
III & IV
I & II
Trpt. in B♭
III
Trb. I & II
Trb. III & Tuba
Trb. III
Timp.
Perc.
S.D.
Vln. I
Vln. II
Vle.
Celli
C. B.
a 2
sul G
arco
cresc.
p sub.
BBb

Here Satan falls out of Heaven. (Blake XVI) Black out and Curtain.

CCc
Fl. I & II
Picc.
Ob.
C. A.
Cl. in B♭
B. Cl. in B♭
Fag.
C. Fag.
I & II
Hns. in F
III & IV
I & II
Trpt. in B♭
III
Trb. I & II
Trb. III & Tuba
Timp.
Perc.
S.D.
Vln. I
Vln. II
Vle.
Celli
C.B.
CCc

ALTAR DANCE

Curtain rises. Enter (on earth) Young men and Women playing on instruments; others bring stones and build an altar. Others dec-orate the altar with flowers (see Blake XXI). But Job must not play on an instrument himself.

DDd
Job blesses the altar (see Blake XVIII).
Fl. I & II
Fl. III
Ob.
C.A.
Cl. I & II in B♭
Cl. III in B♭
Fag.
C.Fag.
I & II
Hns. in F
III & IV
I & II
Trpt. in B♭
III
Trb. I & II
Trb. III & Tuba
Timp.
Perc.
Harp I
Harp II
Vln. I
Vln. II
Vle.
Celli
C.B.
cantabile
a2
p cantabile
Cl. III take Bass Cl.
unis.
sul G.
mp cantabile
pizz.
DDd

The Heavenly dance begins again, while the dance on earth continues.

Fl. I & II
Picc.
Ob.
C.A.
Cl. in B♭
B. Cl. in B♭
Fag.
C. Fag.
I & II
Hns. in F
III & IV
I & II
Trpt. in B♭
III
Trb. I & II
Trb. III & Tuba
Timp.
Perc.
Glock.
Harp I
Harp II
Vln. I
Vln. II
Vle.
Celli
C.B.
Trpt. III
a 2
pp
pp cantabile
tr
B.D.
ppp
div.

Fl. I & II
Picc.
Ob.
C. A.
Cl. in B♭
B. Cl. in B♭
Fag.
C. Fag.
I & II
Hns. in F
III & IV
I & II
Trpt. in B♭
III
Trb. I & II
Trb. III & Tuba
Timp.
Perc.
Glock.
Harp I
Harp II
Vln. I
Vln. II
Vle.
Celli
C. B.
a 2
pp cantabile
pp
unis.
arco
pizz.

FFf
Fl. I & II
Picc.
Ob.
C.A.
Cl. in B♭
B.Cl. in B♭
Fag.
C. Fag.
I & II
Hns. in F
III & IV
I & II
Trpt. in B♭
III
Trb. I & II
Trb. III & Tuba
Timp.
Perc.
B.D.
Glock.
Harp I
Harp II
Vln. I
Vln. II
Vle.
Celli
C. B.
pp cresc.
pp
cresc.
a 2
arco
FFf

Tableau
Lento (𝅗𝅥=72)
Gradual black out
Fl. I & II
Picc.
Ob.
C. A.
Cl. in B♭
B.Cl. in B♭
Fag.
C. Fag.
I & II
Hns. in F
III & IV
I & II
Trpt. in B♭
III
Trb. I & II
Trb. III & Tuba
Timp.
Perc.
Glock.
Harp I
Harp II
Vln. I
Vln. II
Vle.
Celli
C.B.
Take Bass Flute
a 2
Trpt. III
B.D.
Cym.
Mutes on
Mutes on
Mutes on
Mutes on
Lento (𝅗𝅥=72)

SCENE IX
EPILOGUE

Stage lights up again shewing the same scene as the opening. Job an old and humbled man sits with his wife. His friends come up one by one and give him presents (see Blake XIX).

Largo sostenuto (♩ = 48)

FLUTES I & II — ppp

BASS FLUTE in G — Bass Flute in G — pp molto sostenuto

OBOES — ppp

COR ANGLAIS — ppp

CLARINET in B♭ — ppp

BASS CLARINET in B♭ — ppp

FAGOTTI I & II — ppp — Bass Flute I — pp molto sostenuto

CONTRAFFAGOTTO — ppp

HORNS in F — I & II — Mutes on — ppp — III & IV — III Mute on — pppp

TRUMPETS in B♭ — I & II — ppp — III — ppp

TROMBONES — I & II — ppp — III & TUBA — ppp

TIMPANI — A♭ in B♭ — ppp

PERCUSSION — ppp

GLOCKENSPIEL

HARP I

HARP II

VIOLINI I — con sord. sost. — pp

VIOLINI II — con sord — pp

VIOLE — con sord sost. — pp — div

VIOLONCELLI — pp con sord — div — consord.

CONTRABASSI — Mutes on — ppp — div consord. — pizz ppp

Largo sostenuto (♩ = 48)

105

GGg
Job stands and gazes on the distant cornfields
Fl. I & II
B. Fl. in G
Ob.
C. A.
Bass Flute
ppp
Cl. in B♭
1st SOLO
B Cl. in B♭
Fag.
1st SOLO
C. Fag.
I & II
Hns. in F
III & IV
I SOLO
con sord.
III SOLO
con sord.
III mute off
Harp I
Sounds 8ve higher
pp
Harp II
Vln. I
Vln. II
Vle.
unis.
Celli
C. B
GGg

Enter gradually Job's three daughters

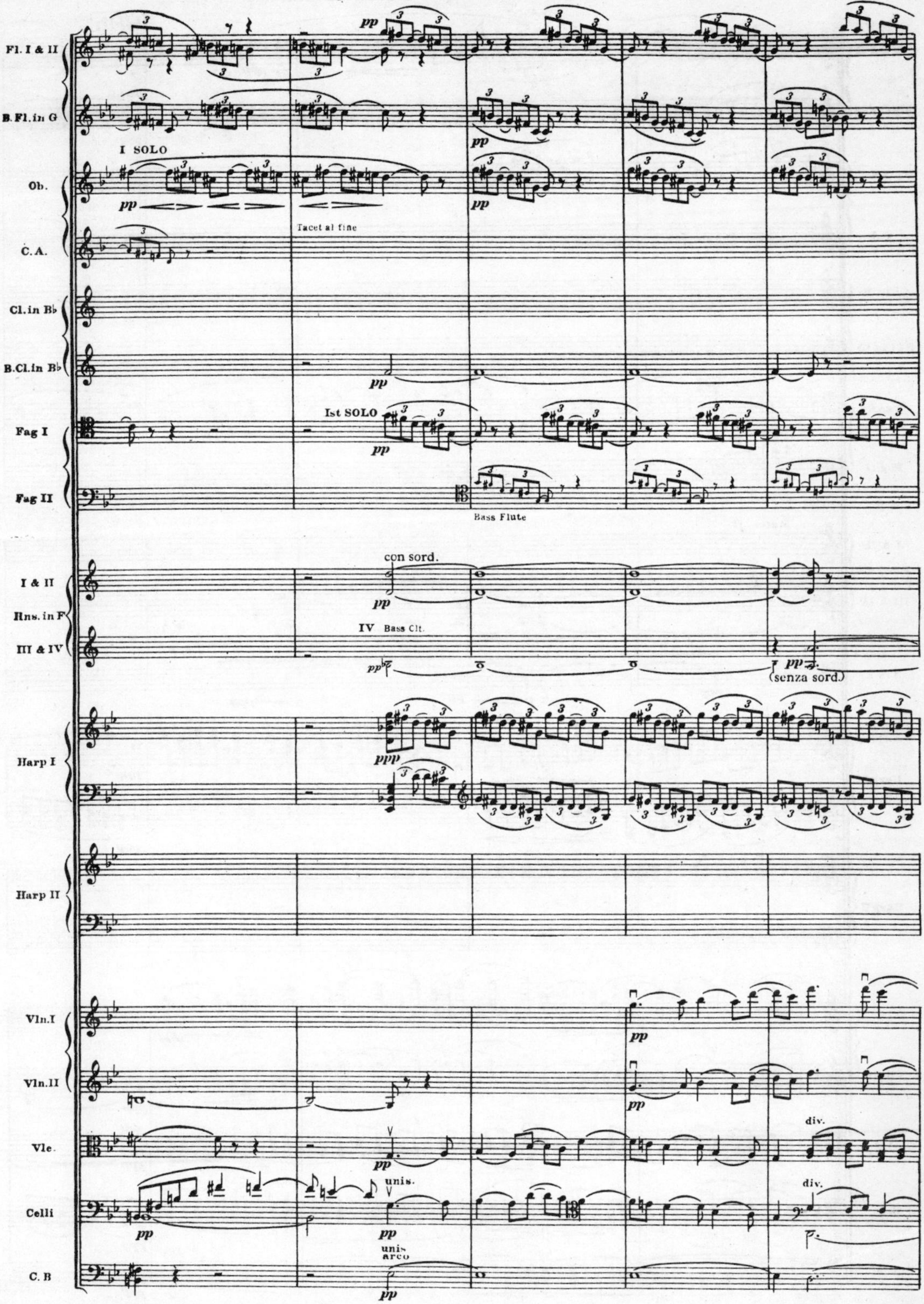

They sit at his feet. He stands and blesses them. (see Blake XX)

HHh

Very slow curtain, and black out
a tempo
rit.
Fl. I & II
B.Fl. in G
Ob.
I SOLO
C.A.
Cl. in B♭
B. Cl. in B♭
Fag. I
Fag. II
Bass Clt
senza sord.
I & II
Hns. in F
III & IV
Timp.
niente
Harp I
Harp II
8va bassa
Vln. I
Vln. II
Vle.
Celli
C.B.
div.
pizz.
(arco)
niente
[only when no harp II]
rit.
a tempo